WORK FOR THE
REFERRAL
NOT THE COMMISSION

THIS WORKBOOK & PLANNER WILL GENERATE REFERRALS FOR:

_____

Offord & Associates Real Estate LLC
www.kimberlyofford.com

Published by Offord & Associates Real Estate LLC
Email: info@kimberlyofford.com
www.kimberlyofford.com

Although the publisher and author have made every effort to ensure that the information in this book was correct at press time and while this publication is designed to provide accurate information in regard to the subject matter covered, the publisher and the author assume no responsibility for errors, inaccuracies, omissions, or any other inconsistencies herein and hereby disclaim any liability to any party for any loss, damage, or disruption caused by errors or omissions, whether such errors or omissions result from negligence, accident, or any other cause.

This publication is meant as a source of valuable information for the reader, however it is not meant as a substitute for direct expert assistance or prevailing state real estate licensing laws of the reader's practicing state.

CONGRATULATIONS!

You are on your way to developing a solid referral based business!

My name is Kimberly Offord and I am so excited to share what I have learned over the past 15 years as a licensed REALTOR® in the state of Illinois. When I started in the real estate business, I had no idea how I would get clients. I just knew that my marketing degrees would soon be put to the test.

Since then, I have tried just about every lead generating strategy known to real estate. I am qualified to say, none compare to the reliable organic leads that derive from a referral. Through 15 years of trial and error, success and failures, I can confidently say that almost 90% of my business is referral based.

In this workbook and planner, I will show you how to write and implement a plan to get more real estate referral leads. The goal is to supplement and eventually replace your current marketing with a solid referral based business. I want each of you to be successful with a business that keeps giving.

Remember, "work for the referral, not the commission!"

Kimberly Offord

Kimberly Offord
IL Licensed REALTOR®
Real Estate Coach, Author

Contents

Let's Start Generating Referrals!

REALITY CHECK

88% of Buyers purchased their home through a real estate agent or broker.

Nice!

91% of Buyers would use their agent again or recommend their agent to others.

89% of Sellers were assisted by a Real Estate Agent when selling their home.

WOW!

74% of Sellers definitely would use the agent again.

41% of sellers who used a real estate agent found their agents through a referral by friends or family.

Wait! Why are these #s Lower?

26% of sellers used the agent they previously worked with to buy or sell a home.

SOURCE: 2020 National Association of Realtors Profile of Home Buyers and Sellers

REALITY CHECK

The stats validate the theory that agents do not understand the value of creating and maintaining referral based marketing.

So let's look at this again:

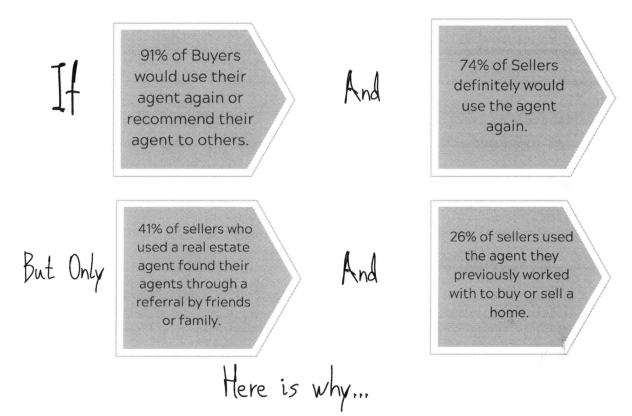

If **91% of Buyers would use their agent again or recommend their agent to others.**

And **74% of Sellers definitely would use the agent again.**

But Only **41% of sellers who used a real estate agent found their agents through a referral by friends or family.**

And **26% of sellers used the agent they previously worked with to buy or sell a home.**

Here is why...

Agents who worked with buyers and sellers had no referral based marketing plan in place to maintain contact and stay front of mind with their past clients. They were focused on the next sale from a new client.

The Original Agent Didn't Get The Referral Because...

The Client lost touch with their agent.

The Client forgot about their agent.

The Client could not find their agent.

No one knew the agent existed!

What is a Referral?

A Referral is someone who uses a product or service based on the recommendation or testimony of another person they know, like or trust.

THE GOAL ⟶

When you reach the point where the majority of your business is based on referrals, you have a **Referral Based Business**.

Why is having a referral based business important?

- Increases revenue
- Creates loyalty
- Reduces the cost of marketing
- Increases lead conversion
- Reduces or eliminates "cold calling" lead generation methods
- Builds your brand
- Strengthens your position in the market

Many companies have business models that support a referral system.

Tesla   Evernote   DropBox   Uber   AirBnB   PayPal   Amazon Prime

---

What are some referral programs you have supported?
Why did you refer the product or service?

_____

_____

_____

_____

NOTES

Work For the Referral Not the Commission

What does it mean to work for the referral and not the commission?

Our Code of Ethics and local real estate license laws dictate that we work with the best interest of the client in mind. Our decisions are based on ethics and honoring our fiduciary duties.

However, there are times when agents are tempted to "chase the commission." Those are the days when we haven't closed any transactions in a month or more and money is low. Maybe you are one sale away from making "Top Producer" and the primary focus is on closing the deal no matter what. Chasing after the commission can lead to slacking on other responsibilities to the client.

Remove the focus from counting the commission and place it back on the quality of service rendered to the public. When you are operating on this level, **it means you are providing value to your client's experience. Value is rewarded with referrals.**

Your marketing strategy will shift to targeting people who already know, like and trust you. They will be your biggest cheerleaders and lead generators.

That is what it means to work for the referral, not the commission.

How is a Referral Born?

Chain of events that can lead to a referral:

- Someone has a positive experience with their real estate agent.
- Someone is asked if they know of a good real estate agent.
- A social media supporter recalls a post about real estate.
- A service partner sends one of their clients to a real estate agent.
- A real estate agent refers a client in a different market.

For the referral to occur you must:

- Provide great service
- Make it known that you are a REALTOR®
- ASK for the referral
- Stay in contact with your former clients
- Network with REALTORS® in other markets
- Give referrals to other service providers

 FOOD FOR THOUGHT

"No one needs a real estate agent until they need a real estate agent. Therefore, you need to be the real estate agent they think about when they finally realize they need a real estate agent"

Kimberly Offord

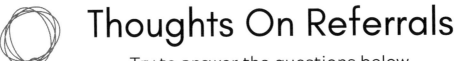

Thoughts On Referrals

Try to answer the questions below.
Use the notes page to write down your thoughts.

Do your friends, family and acquaintances know you are a real estate agent ?

Are you comfortable asking for referrals?

Have you asked anyone for referrals in the past year?

How often do you ask for referrals?

How many referrals have you received in the past year?

Who has sent referrals to you in the past?

Did you thank those who sent you referrals?

Do you have any marketing that specifically asks for a referral?

Do you have a database or somewhere to store your contacts?

Have you sent any referrals to other businesses/services? If so, who were those services and have they sent you referrals in return?

NOTES

Those Most Likely to Refer You

Past/Current Clients ⟶ Buyers & Sellers you have worked with that have 1st hand knowledge of your services.

Sphere of Influence ⟶ Your personal cheerleaders who have vested interest in your success. People who know, like and trust you. They may or may not be clients. Includes friends and family members.

Service Partners ⟶ Attorneys, Lenders, Contractors, Inspectors, etc. (any real estate related professional whose services you refer.)

Other Real Estate Agents ⟶ Real Estate Agents in other markets or expertise who may have clients they refer to you.

 REMEMBER

Our focus is on referrals from one of the above groups. We are not focusing on forms of paid advertising, marketing or lead generation efforts to consumers we don't know personally. We are not suggesting these methods be abandoned. The goal is to build multiple lead sources. Referrals are one of many.

Start with a Good Database

Now is a good time to emphasize how critical it is to have a database. If your brokerage provides a CRM (customer relationship management) system, USE IT! If not, there are several in the market that you can subscribe to on your own. There are some that have free versions and others that can go as high as $300 a month. If you can't afford one at this time, a simple spreadsheet will work fine.

Make a list of everyone who has referred you in the past and those who you believe would refer you if asked. **List them together according to the categories below.**

Categories:

- Past Client
- Current Client
- Sphere of Influence
- Service Partners
- Real Estate Agents

What to Look for in a CRM
(The Essentials)

- Drip Campaign
- Marketing Auto Pilot
- Landing/Squeeze Pages
- Website
- IDX Service (MLS)

 THINK ABOUT THIS

Build a list of 75-100 people who know, like and trust you. If just 10 people on that list would refer you to someone who will use you as their agent, your existing business would increase by 10 transactions that year. Think of how much that could be in commissions.

Activity: Make a List

Information You Will Need to Gather

To get started, a solid database can be built with the bare minimums:

Name (First and Last)
Cell Phone
Email Address
Mailing Address
(at least 2 contact methods)

For a more thorough and robust approach, you can include additional information that will enhance your referral marketing efforts. Here are some suggestions to get you started:

Birthday
Anniversary Dates
Children or Spouses Birthday
Community Interests
Hobbies or Special Interest
Occupation

It will be explained in the upcoming sections why this is important.

CAUTION

When creating your list remember: Do not add people you are unsure would support you. Check the DO NOT CALL lists even for those you know. Don't spam your contacts. Make sure you have a method for contacts to either ask to be removed or to remove themselves.

NOTES

Goals For Your List

Think of your list like a tree that will bear fruit. Remember these four key factors to keep your list alive and generating referral leads.

Become a Resource & Expert

Your list must be nurtured.

In order for your list to provide results, you need to stay in contact on a regular (not frequent) basis. Use your list to provide information, celebrate special occasions and to remind your contacts you are available for their real estate needs.

Contacts Want to Be on Your List

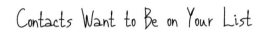

The list must grow.

You should add prospects, clients, friends, family, service partners and referral brokers to your contact list continuously. Lead Pages and subscriber links work well. DO NOT pay for a list. Your leads should be people who know, like, trust and **want** to hear from you.

Keep Your List Relevant

The list must be trimmed as it grows.

Remove old, inactive, out-dated contact information and any contacts who asked to be removed from the list. Your list should be strictly QUALITY over quantity. Review your list regularly and trim as needed. Don't worry, it will grow!

Ask for the Referral!

The list must bear fruit.

Your list should generate referrals. As you develop your list, keep track of who sends referrals. Our initial goal is to generate referrals from at least 10% of your total contact list. As your list grows, that rate will increase.

NOTES

Setting Goals

Now that referrals will become a significant contributor to your overall marketing goals, set quantitive goals. Think of how your referral business can supplement and eventually replace your traditional lead generation system.

Business Planning

1. What are your overall financial goals for this year? Dream Big!

2. What is the average price of properties in your market?

3. What is your average commission percentage earned per sale?

4. Multiply line 3 by line 2. Then factor in fees and commission splits. This is your average earnings per sale.

5. Divide Line 1 by line 4. This is the number of closing you will need to reach your financial goals for this year.

Referral Projected Goals

6. Total number of contacts you have in your database/CRM system.

7. Multiply the number of contacts by 10%. This is the goal number of contacts that will send you referral business.

8. What percentage of your leads close? Multiply line 7 by the appropriate percentage. This is the number of referral deals you could close this year.

9. Multiply line 8 by line 4. This is your income earned from referral business alone.

See sample worksheet on the next page.

Setting Goals

Working Example

Here is an example of a completed goal sheet.

Business Planning - EXAMPLE

1. What are your overall financial goals for this year?

   $100,000.00

2. What is the average price of properties in your market?

   $200,000.00

3. What is your average commission percentage earned per sale?

   3%

4. Multiply line 3 by line 2. Then factor in brokerage fees and commission splits. This is your average earnings per sale.

   $6,000

5. Divide Line 1 by line 4. This is the number of closing you will need to reach your financial goals for this year.

   17

Referral Projected Goals

6. Total number of contacts you have in your database/CRM system.

   100

7. Multiply the number of contacts by 10%. This is the goal number of contacts that will send you referral business.

   10

8. What percentage of your leads close? **Let's assume you close at least 50%. Multiply line 7 by 50%.** This is the projected number of referral deals you will close this year.

   5

9. Multiply line 8 by line 4. This is your projected income earned from referral business.

   $30,000

In this example, referrals could earn $30,000 in income!

Nurturing Your List
Touch Points

You have a list. You have monetary goals. Now it is time to develop strategies to nurture your referral business. By staying in contact, reminding your contacts of your services and providing valuable information, you can stay front of mind through touch points.

A **Touch Point** is any time someone comes in contact with you, your message, brand or marketing. This can be anytime before or after the real estate transaction is completed.

Think about your favorite brand. How many times in a day, week or month and in how many different ways do you come in contact with that brand name or image? Here are some of the most common ways below:

Television/Radio
Commercials, Sponsorships, cable, network, satellite etc.

Direct Marketing
Email, Postcards, Catalogues, Letters, Newsletters, Flyers, Brochures etc.

Apparel
Shirts, Hats, Everyday household items etc.

Social Media
Fan Pages, Posts, Live Video, Tweets, Recorded Video, Paid Ads, Sponsorships etc.

Events
Concerts, Festivals, Seminars, Conferences etc.

Creating Touch Points

**"No one needs a Realtor until they need a Realtor.
Therefore, you need to be the Realtor they think about when
they finally realize they need a Realtor"**

Your Goal ⟶ **Create MULTIPLE Touch Points Throughout the Year**

For the next twelve months, your goal is to stay front of mind with your sphere so that when there is a need for a real estate professional, you are the first they call. This is achieved when your brand is exposed to your target audience multiple times and in multiple ways over a course of time.

The Essentials - Reaching Potential Referral Sources
Here are some of the essential touch points every real estate professional should incorporate into their marketing:

Social Media
Direct Mail
Personal Touches
Email & Text Messaging
Community Involvement

The internet has become the primary location for consumers to shop for a property. While there are several ways to reach your core sphere of influence electronically, never underestimate the effectiveness of an old fashioned handwritten note. The next page will explore the essential touch points closer.

The Essential Touches

Social Media

Social media is one of the easiest and FREE ways to stay top of mind within your sphere of influence. Here are just a few tips:

- Follow your contacts on social media, celebrate their anniversaries, wish them happy birthday, interact on posts.
- Post often about real estate, your niche market and personal interests. Post live and recorded video.
- Establish a business page on your preferred social media.
- Understand which social media platforms are best for you.
- Understand which social media platform is used by your sphere.
- Be consistent, use hashtags and always ASK for referrals.
- Schedule social media posts in advance with syndication applications.
- Join social media groups to network with real estate agents in other markets. They are a great source for referral income.

Direct Mail

Direct mail pieces should be sent periodically throughout the year to generate referral business. Some include:

- Postcards, Promotional Letters
- Handwritten Notes, Holiday Cards

Personal Touch

Think of unique personalized ways to stay front of mind. For example:

- Invitations to coffee or lunch
- Care packages
- Customer appreciation events
- Phone Calls

The Essential Touches

Email & Text Messaging

With the ability to send text messages and other innovative forms of communication, email marketing doesn't have the same reach as it once did. However, it should not be ignored. Use email to support other efforts.

- Drip Campaigns (Email & Text)
- Email Newsletters
- Market Reports and Property Searches

Community Involvement

Get involved in causes that matter to you. Give the same support you are seeking to local businesses and nonprofits. Become the **involved** neighborhood expert of your chosen community. **Refer other service providers** to your friends and loved ones. **Get involved in the real estate community!** Network with Realtors in other cities and niche' markets. Remember, referrals are a gift that keeps giving.

The next step: Develop a calendar where your brand is exposed to your target **at least 16 times each quarter** over the next 12 mo.

This plan is very heavily based on social media marketing and one-on-one interaction. You wont need to be an expert, but you will definitely need to be familiar with the various platforms.

For more information on navigating social media, don't hesitate to refer to the various social media experts for advice. I would recommend Social Media Gurus Marki Lemons Ryhal, www.markilemons.com and Carrie J. Little, www.carrielittle.com.

THE 16 TOUCH PLAN

At a minimum, target 75-100 people in your sphere (friends, family, past clients, service partners). This will be the CORE group. Follow the touch plan for 12 months.

Touch Goal ⟶ 16 Touches A Quarter

Social Media
Daily Activity

Post to social media **at least** 3x's a week (Everyday life, information, celebrations, sales, inspiration, post interactions, live/recorded video, stories etc)

Direct Mail
At Least 1 A Quarter

Schedule **at least** 1 mass mailing to your core sphere group during the quarter (Post Card, Handwritten Note or Holiday Card)

Personal Touch
Weekly Activity

Call at least 5-10 people in Sphere of Influence weekly. Invite to lunch or coffee, send dinner gift card, ask for referrals

Email/Text
Monthly Activity

Set up a drip campaign within your CRM system. Be careful not to spam anyone with unwanted email. Provide valuable information.

Community Involvement
Monthly Activity

To get referrals, you must give referrals. Highlight or refer at least 4 businesses or service partners every month.

Remember the goal is to build a referral based business while also building your database.

Suggested Touch Points

1. Send Branded Newsletter
2. Send Monthly Postcards
3. Send A Handwritten Note
4. Send a Market Report
5. Get Written Reviews From Past Clients
6. Meet with Your Sphere for Coffee
7. Create An Email Drip Campaign
8. Send Text Message Asking For Referrals
9. Make Calls to 5-10 Contacts a Week
10. Offer to do a CMA on Property
11. Send Handwritten Holiday Cards
12. Send a Video Message
13. Post About Listings on Social Media
14. Post About Closings on Social Media
15. Post About Every Day Life Events on Social Media
16. Post live Social Media Content
17. Create a Video and Post to Social Media
18. Comment/Interact on Other Social Media Posts
19. "Boost" a Social Media Post
20. Post in a Social Media Group for Real Estate Consumers
21. Network with other Realtors on Social Media
22. Purchase Social Media Ads
23. Host a Client Appreciation Event
24. Send Care Packages to Previous Clients
25. Send Referrals To Preferred Partners
26. Volunteer in the Community (Take Pictures and Post to Social media)
27. Sponsor Community a Event
28. Host Educational and Seminars Events
29. Celebrate New Homeowners on Social Media
30. Celebrate Anniversary of Home Purchase of Previous Clients
31. Provide Information on Home Buying & Selling Process
32. Provide Information on Real Estate Investments
33. Sponsor a Virtual/In-Person Open House
34. Host a Video Housewarming
35. Host a Video Open House

NOTES

Quarter 1 Planning

Getting Started

Included: Sample Goal and Planner
Your First 13 Weeks

 # Quarter 1 Goals

Referrals Goal This Quarter
Remember to refer to your goal projections sheet

# of Referrals Received Last Quarter

Referral Leads Converted to Business

Commission Earned from Referral Business

4

2

1

$3,200

☑ <u>Core Activities (Consistent Activities)</u>

☑ Post on Social Media 3xs a week

☑ Call 5-10 Contacts in Sphere of Influence a week

☑ Refer business to at least 7 other service partners during the quarter.

<u>Your Pick (Activities of Your Choice) 4x4 = 16</u>

Pick 4 other touch points to implement 4xs time during **the quarter**.

☑ Touch Point 1 *Send Handwritten Notes w/Bus. Card - Ask for Referrals!*

☑ Touch Point 2 *Take 5-10 Sphere for Coffee & Ask For Referrals*

☑ Touch Point 3 *Send Monthly Newsletter*

☑ Touch Point 4 *Send Market Reports & Ask For Referrals*

WEEKLY PLANNER
Week 1

MONDAY

Complete Sphere of Influence Calls
Post a Motivation to Social Media

TUESDAY

Write 10 Handwritten Notes to Sphere

WEDNESDAY

Social Media Post about New Listing
(Ask for Referrals)

THURSDAY

Showings with Clients

FRIDAY

Showings with Clients

SATURDAY

Post about Closing!! (Ask for Referrals)
Schedule Social Media Posts for Next Week

SUNDAY

R E S T ! ! !
Family/Personal Time

TO DO

- [x] Post on Social Media 3xs
- [x] Complete Touch Point Activity
- [x] Add Contacts to Database
- [x] Ask for Referrals
- [ ] Review Goals
- [ ] Refer Another Business
- [x] Plan For Next Week

SPHERE OF INFLUENCE CALLS

1. Jane Doe - Trainer
2. John Smith - Past Client
3. Bob Black - Church Member
4. Mary Brown - Family Friend
5. Sue Davis - Past Client - Birthday!

NOTES

Follow up with Bill for coffee this week.

Send Carla a Thank-You note for the referral.

Add Referral David B. to database.

Quarter 1 Goals

THE 16 TOUCH PLAN

Referral Goals This Quarter
Remember to refer to your goal projections sheet   _____

# of Referrals Received Last Quarter   _____

Referral Leads Converted to Business   _____

Commission Earned from Referral Business   _____

Core Activities (Consistent Activities)
☑ Post on Social Media 3xs a week

☑ Call 2-5 Contacts in Sphere of Influence a week

☑ Refer business to at least 7 other service partners during the quarter.

Your Pick (Activities of Your Choice) 4x4=16
Pick 4 other touch points to implement 4xs time during the quarter.

☑ Touch Point 1 _____

☑ Touch Point 2 _____

☑ Touch Point 3 _____

☑ Touch Point 4 _____

WEEKLY PLANNER
Week 1
Date_____

MONDAY

TUESDAY

WEDNESDAY

THURSDAY

FRIDAY

SATURDAY

SUNDAY

TO DO

☐ Post on Social Media at least 3xs

☐ Complete Touch Point Activity

☐ Add Contacts to Database

☐ Ask for Referrals

☐ Review Goals

☐ Refer Another Business

☐ Plan For Next Week

SPHERE OF INFLUENCE CALLS

1.
2.
3.
4.
5.

NOTES

WEEKLY PLANNER
Week 2

Date_____

MONDAY

TUESDAY

WEDNESDAY

THURSDAY

FRIDAY

SATURDAY

SUNDAY

TO DO

- [ ] Post on Social Media at least 3xs
- [ ] Complete Touch Point Activity
- [ ] Add Contacts to Database
- [ ] Ask for Referrals
- [ ] Review Goals
- [ ] Refer Another Business
- [ ] Plan For Next Week

SPHERE OF INFLUENCE CALLS

1.
2.
3.
4.
5.

NOTES

WEEKLY PLANNER
Week 3

Date_____

MONDAY

TUESDAY

WEDNESDAY

THURSDAY

FRIDAY

SATURDAY

SUNDAY

TO DO

- [ ] Post on Social Media at least 3xs
- [ ] Complete Touch Point Activity
- [ ] Add Contacts to Database
- [ ] Ask for Referrals
- [ ] Review Goals
- [ ] Refer Another Business
- [ ] Plan For Next Week

SPHERE OF INFLUENCE CALLS

1.
2.
3.
4.
5.

NOTES

WEEKLY PLANNER
Week 4

Date_____

MONDAY

TUESDAY

WEDNESDAY

THURSDAY

FRIDAY

SATURDAY

SUNDAY

TO DO

- [ ] Post on Social Media at least 3xs
- [ ] Complete Touch Point Activity
- [ ] Add Contacts to Database
- [ ] Ask for Referrals
- [ ] Review Goals
- [ ] Refer Another Business
- [ ] Plan For Next Week

SPHERE OF INFLUENCE CALLS

1.
2.
3.
4.
5.

NOTES

WEEKLY PLANNER
Week 5

Date_____

MONDAY

TUESDAY

WEDNESDAY

THURSDAY

FRIDAY

SATURDAY

SUNDAY

TO DO

- [ ] Post on Social Media at least 3xs
- [ ] Complete Touch Point Activity
- [ ] Add Contacts to Database
- [ ] Ask for Referrals
- [ ] Review Goals
- [ ] Refer Another Business
- [ ] Plan For Next Week

SPHERE OF INFLUENCE CALLS

1.
2.
3.
4.
5.

NOTES

WEEKLY PLANNER
Week 6
Date_____

MONDAY

TUESDAY

WEDNESDAY

THURSDAY

FRIDAY

SATURDAY

SUNDAY

TO DO

- [ ] Post on Social Media at least 3xs
- [ ] Complete Touch Point Activity
- [ ] Add Contacts to Database
- [ ] Ask for Referrals
- [ ] Review Goals
- [ ] Refer Another Business
- [ ] Plan For Next Week

SPHERE OF INFLUENCE CALLS

1.
2.
3.
4.
5.

NOTES

WEEKLY PLANNER
Week 7

Date_____

MONDAY

TUESDAY

WEDNESDAY

THURSDAY

FRIDAY

SATURDAY

SUNDAY

TO DO

☐ Post on Social Media at least 3xs

☐ Complete Touch Point Activity

☐ Add Contacts to Database

☐ Ask for Referrals

☐ Review Goals

☐ Refer Another Business

☐ Plan For Next Week

SPHERE OF INFLUENCE CALLS

1.

2.

3.

4.

5.

NOTES

WEEKLY PLANNER
Week 8

Date_____

MONDAY

TUESDAY

WEDNESDAY

THURSDAY

FRIDAY

SATURDAY

SUNDAY

TO DO

- [ ] Post on Social Media at least 3xs
- [ ] Complete Touch Point Activity
- [ ] Add Contacts to Database
- [ ] Ask for Referrals
- [ ] Review Goals
- [ ] Refer Another Business
- [ ] Plan For Next Week

SPHERE OF INFLUENCE CALLS

1.
2.
3.
4.
5.

NOTES

WEEKLY PLANNER
Week 9

Date_____

MONDAY

TUESDAY

WEDNESDAY

THURSDAY

FRIDAY

SATURDAY

SUNDAY

TO DO

☐ Post on Social Media at least 3xs

☐ Complete Touch Point Activity

☐ Add Contacts to Database

☐ Ask for Referrals

☐ Review Goals

☐ Refer Another Business

☐ Plan For Next Week

SPHERE OF INFLUENCE CALLS

1.
2.
3.
4.
5.

NOTES

WEEKLY PLANNER
Week 10

Date_____

MONDAY

TUESDAY

WEDNESDAY

THURSDAY

FRIDAY

SATURDAY

SUNDAY

TO DO

- [ ] Post on Social Media at least 3xs
- [ ] Complete Touch Point Activity
- [ ] Add Contacts to Database
- [ ] Ask for Referrals
- [ ] Review Goals
- [ ] Refer Another Business
- [ ] Plan For Next Week

SPHERE OF INFLUENCE CALLS

1.
2.
3.
4.
5.

NOTES

WEEKLY PLANNER
Week 11   Date_____

MONDAY

TUESDAY

WEDNESDAY

THURSDAY

FRIDAY

SATURDAY

SUNDAY

TO DO

- [ ] Post on Social Media at least 3xs
- [ ] Complete Touch Point Activity
- [ ] Add Contacts to Database
- [ ] Ask for Referrals
- [ ] Review Goals
- [ ] Refer Another Business
- [ ] Plan For Next Week

SPHERE OF INFLUENCE CALLS

1.
2.
3.
4.
5.

NOTES

WEEKLY PLANNER
Week 12

Date_____

MONDAY

TUESDAY

WEDNESDAY

THURSDAY

FRIDAY

SATURDAY

SUNDAY

TO DO

- [ ] Post on Social Media at least 3xs
- [ ] Complete Touch Point Activity
- [ ] Add Contacts to Database
- [ ] Ask for Referrals
- [ ] Review Goals
- [ ] Refer Another Business
- [ ] Plan For Next Week

SPHERE OF INFLUENCE CALLS

1.
2.
3.
4.
5.

NOTES

WEEKLY PLANNER
Week 13

Date_____

MONDAY

TUESDAY

WEDNESDAY

THURSDAY

FRIDAY

SATURDAY

SUNDAY

TO DO

- ☐ Post on Social Media at least 3xs
- ☐ Complete Touch Point Activity
- ☐ Add Contacts to Database
- ☐ Ask for Referrals
- ☐ Review Goals
- ☐ Refer Another Business
- ☐ Plan For Next Week

SPHERE OF INFLUENCE CALLS

1.
2.
3.
4.
5.

NOTES

Quarter 1 Recap

What worked well?

Which activity did you feel most comfortable performing? Why?

Which activity was the least comfortable? Why?

Was it difficult or easy asking for referrals? Why?

How many referral leads did you receive over the past quarter?

Did you meet any new service partners you can refer to your sphere?

Did your database grow?

What adjustments need to be made for the next quarter?

Quarter 2
Planner

☑ Quarter 2 Goals

Referral Goals This Quarter
Remember to refer to your goal projections sheet

# of Referrals Received Last Quarter

Referral Leads Converted to Business

Commission Earned from Referral Business

_____

_____

_____

_____

Core Activities   (Consistent Activities)

☑ Post on Social Media 3xs a week

☑ Call 2-5 Contacts in Sphere of Influence a week

☑ Refer business to at least 7 other service partners during the quarter.

Your Pick   (Activities of Your Choice) 4X4=16
Pick 4 other touch points to implement 4xs time during the quarter.

☑ Touch Point 1
_____

☑ Touch Point 2
_____

☑ Touch Point 3
_____

☑ Touch Point 4
_____

WEEKLY PLANNER
Week 14   Date_____

MONDAY

TUESDAY

WEDNESDAY

THURSDAY

FRIDAY

SATURDAY

SUNDAY

TO DO

- [ ] Post on Social Media at least 3xs
- [ ] Complete Touch Point Activity
- [ ] Add Contacts to Database
- [ ] Ask for Referrals
- [ ] Review Goals
- [ ] Refer Another Business
- [ ] Plan For Next Week

SPHERE OF INFLUENCE CALLS

1.
2.
3.
4.
5.

NOTES

WEEKLY PLANNER
Week 15

Date_____

MONDAY

TUESDAY

WEDNESDAY

THURSDAY

FRIDAY

SATURDAY

SUNDAY

TO DO

- [ ] Post on Social Media at least 3xs
- [ ] Complete Touch Point Activity
- [ ] Add Contacts to Database
- [ ] Ask for Referrals
- [ ] Review Goals
- [ ] Refer Another Business
- [ ] Plan For Next Week

SPHERE OF INFLUENCE CALLS

1.
2.
3.
4.
5.

NOTES

WEEKLY PLANNER
Week 16

Date_____

MONDAY

TUESDAY

WEDNESDAY

THURSDAY

FRIDAY

SATURDAY

SUNDAY

TO DO

- ☐ Post on Social Media at least 3xs
- ☐ Complete Touch Point Activity
- ☐ Add Contacts to Database
- ☐ Ask for Referrals
- ☐ Review Goals
- ☐ Refer Another Business
- ☐ Plan For Next Week

SPHERE OF INFLUENCE CALLS

1.
2.
3.
4.
5.

NOTES

WEEKLY PLANNER
Week 17

Date_____

MONDAY

TUESDAY

WEDNESDAY

THURSDAY

FRIDAY

SATURDAY

SUNDAY

TO DO

- [ ] Post on Social Media at least 3xs
- [ ] Complete Touch Point Activity
- [ ] Add Contacts to Database
- [ ] Ask for Referrals
- [ ] Review Goals
- [ ] Refer Another Business
- [ ] Plan For Next Week

SPHERE OF INFLUENCE CALLS

1.
2.
3.
4.
5.

NOTES

WEEKLY PLANNER
Week 18

Date_____

MONDAY

TUESDAY

WEDNESDAY

THURSDAY

FRIDAY

SATURDAY

SUNDAY

TO DO

- [ ] Post on Social Media at least 3xs
- [ ] Complete Touch Point Activity
- [ ] Add Contacts to Database
- [ ] Ask for Referrals
- [ ] Review Goals
- [ ] Refer Another Business
- [ ] Plan For Next Week

SPHERE OF INFLUENCE CALLS

1.
2.
3.
4.
5.

NOTES

WEEKLY PLANNER
Week 19

Date_____

MONDAY

TUESDAY

WEDNESDAY

THURSDAY

FRIDAY

SATURDAY

SUNDAY

TO DO

- [ ] Post on Social Media at least 3xs
- [ ] Complete Touch Point Activity
- [ ] Add Contacts to Database
- [ ] Ask for Referrals
- [ ] Review Goals
- [ ] Refer Another Business
- [ ] Plan For Next Week

SPHERE OF INFLUENCE CALLS

1.
2.
3.
4.
5.

NOTES

WEEKLY PLANNER

Week 20

Date_____

MONDAY

TUESDAY

WEDNESDAY

THURSDAY

FRIDAY

SATURDAY

SUNDAY

TO DO

- [ ] Post on Social Media at least 3xs
- [ ] Complete Touch Point Activity
- [ ] Add Contacts to Database
- [ ] Ask for Referrals
- [ ] Review Goals
- [ ] Refer Another Business
- [ ] Plan For Next Week

SPHERE OF INFLUENCE CALLS

1.
2.
3.
4.
5.

NOTES

WEEKLY PLANNER
Week 21

Date_____

MONDAY

TUESDAY

WEDNESDAY

THURSDAY

FRIDAY

SATURDAY

SUNDAY

TO DO

- ☐ Post on Social Media at least 3xs
- ☐ Complete Touch Point Activity
- ☐ Add Contacts to Database
- ☐ Ask for Referrals
- ☐ Review Goals
- ☐ Refer Another Business
- ☐ Plan For Next Week

SPHERE OF INFLUENCE CALLS

1.
2.
3.
4.
5.

NOTES

WEEKLY PLANNER
Week 22

Date_____

MONDAY

TUESDAY

WEDNESDAY

THURSDAY

FRIDAY

SATURDAY

SUNDAY

TO DO

- [ ] Post on Social Media at least 3xs
- [ ] Complete Touch Point Activity
- [ ] Add Contacts to Database
- [ ] Ask for Referrals
- [ ] Review Goals
- [ ] Refer Another Business
- [ ] Plan For Next Week

SPHERE OF INFLUENCE CALLS

1.
2.
3.
4.
5.

NOTES

WEEKLY PLANNER
Week 23   Date_____

MONDAY

TUESDAY

WEDNESDAY

THURSDAY

FRIDAY

SATURDAY

SUNDAY

TO DO

- [ ] Post on Social Media at least 3xs
- [ ] Complete Touch Point Activity
- [ ] Add Contacts to Database
- [ ] Ask for Referrals
- [ ] Review Goals
- [ ] Refer Another Business
- [ ] Plan For Next Week

SPHERE OF INFLUENCE CALLS

1.
2.
3.
4.
5.

NOTES

WEEKLY PLANNER
Week 24

Date_____

MONDAY

TUESDAY

WEDNESDAY

THURSDAY

FRIDAY

SATURDAY

SUNDAY

TO DO

- [ ] Post on Social Media at least 3xs
- [ ] Complete Touch Point Activity
- [ ] Add Contacts to Database
- [ ] Ask for Referrals
- [ ] Review Goals
- [ ] Refer Another Business
- [ ] Plan For Next Week

SPHERE OF INFLUENCE CALLS

1.
2.
3.
4.
5.

NOTES

WEEKLY PLANNER
Week 25

Date_____

MONDAY

TUESDAY

WEDNESDAY

THURSDAY

FRIDAY

SATURDAY

SUNDAY

TO DO

- [ ] Post on Social Media at least 3xs
- [ ] Complete Touch Point Activity
- [ ] Add Contacts to Database
- [ ] Ask for Referrals
- [ ] Review Goals
- [ ] Refer Another Business
- [ ] Plan For Next Week

SPHERE OF INFLUENCE CALLS

1.
2.
3.
4.
5.

NOTES

WEEKLY PLANNER
Week 26

Date_____

MONDAY

TUESDAY

WEDNESDAY

THURSDAY

FRIDAY

SATURDAY

SUNDAY

TO DO

- [ ] Post on Social Media at least 3xs
- [ ] Complete Touch Point Activity
- [ ] Add Contacts to Database
- [ ] Ask for Referrals
- [ ] Review Goals
- [ ] Refer Another Business
- [ ] Plan For Next Week

SPHERE OF INFLUENCE CALLS

1.
2.
3.
4.
5.

NOTES

Quarter 2 Recap

What worked well?

Which activity did you feel most comfortable performing? Why?

Which activity was the least comfortable? Why?

Was it difficult or easy asking for referrals? Why?

How many referral leads did you receive over the past quarter?

Did you meet any new service partners you can refer to your sphere?

Did your database grow?

What adjustments need to be made for the next quarter?

Quarter 3
Planner

☑ Quarter 3 Goals

THE 16 TOUCH PLAN

Referral Goals This Quarter
Remember to refer to your goal projections sheet

# of Referrals Received Last Quarter

Referral Leads Converted to Business

Commission Earned from Referral Business

_____

_____

_____

_____

☑ ## Core Activities (Consistent Activities)
Post on Social Media 3xs a week

☑ Call 2-5 Contacts in Sphere of Influence a week

☑ Refer business to at least 7 other service partners during the quarter.

Your Pick (Activities of Your Choice) 4x4=16
Pick 4 other touch points to implement 4xs time during the quarter.

☑ Touch Point 1 _____

☑ Touch Point 2 _____

☑ Touch Point 3 _____

☑ Touch Point 4 _____

WEEKLY PLANNER
Week 27   Date_____

MONDAY

TUESDAY

WEDNESDAY

THURSDAY

FRIDAY

SATURDAY

SUNDAY

TO DO

☐ Post on Social Media at least 3xs

☐ Complete Touch Point Activity

☐ Add Contacts to Database

☐ Ask for Referrals

☐ Review Goals

☐ Refer Another Business

☐ Plan For Next Week

SPHERE OF INFLUENCE CALLS

1.
2.
3.
4.
5.

NOTES

WEEKLY PLANNER
Week 28
Date_____

MONDAY

TUESDAY

WEDNESDAY

THURSDAY

FRIDAY

SATURDAY

SUNDAY

TO DO

- [ ] Post on Social Media at least 3xs
- [ ] Complete Touch Point Activity
- [ ] Add Contacts to Database
- [ ] Ask for Referrals
- [ ] Review Goals
- [ ] Refer Another Business
- [ ] Plan For Next Week

SPHERE OF INFLUENCE CALLS

1.
2.
3.
4.
5.

NOTES

WEEKLY PLANNER
Week 29   Date_____

MONDAY

TUESDAY

WEDNESDAY

THURSDAY

FRIDAY

SATURDAY

SUNDAY

TO DO

☐ Post on Social Media at least 3xs

☐ Complete Touch Point Activity

☐ Add Contacts to Database

☐ Ask for Referrals

☐ Review Goals

☐ Refer Another Business

☐ Plan For Next Week

SPHERE OF INFLUENCE CALLS

1.

2.

3.

4.

5.

NOTES

WEEKLY PLANNER
Week 30

Date_____

MONDAY

TUESDAY

WEDNESDAY

THURSDAY

FRIDAY

SATURDAY

SUNDAY

TO DO

- [ ] Post on Social Media at least 3xs
- [ ] Complete Touch Point Activity
- [ ] Add Contacts to Database
- [ ] Ask for Referrals
- [ ] Review Goals
- [ ] Refer Another Business
- [ ] Plan For Next Week

SPHERE OF INFLUENCE CALLS

1.
2.
3.
4.
5.

NOTES

WEEKLY PLANNER
Week 31

Date_____

MONDAY

TUESDAY

WEDNESDAY

THURSDAY

FRIDAY

SATURDAY

SUNDAY

TO DO

☐ Post on Social Media at least 3xs

☐ Complete Touch Point Activity

☐ Add Contacts to Database

☐ Ask for Referrals

☐ Review Goals

☐ Refer Another Business

☐ Plan For Next Week

SPHERE OF INFLUENCE CALLS

1.
2.
3.
4.
5.

NOTES

WEEKLY PLANNER
Week 32   Date_____

MONDAY

TUESDAY

WEDNESDAY

THURSDAY

FRIDAY

SATURDAY

SUNDAY

TO DO

- ☐ Post on Social Media at least 3xs
- ☐ Complete Touch Point Activity
- ☐ Add Contacts to Database
- ☐ Ask for Referrals
- ☐ Review Goals
- ☐ Refer Another Business
- ☐ Plan For Next Week

SPHERE OF INFLUENCE CALLS

1.
2.
3.
4.
5.

NOTES

WEEKLY PLANNER
Week 33

Date_____

MONDAY

TUESDAY

WEDNESDAY

THURSDAY

FRIDAY

SATURDAY

SUNDAY

TO DO

- ☐ Post on Social Media at least 3xs
- ☐ Complete Touch Point Activity
- ☐ Add Contacts to Database
- ☐ Ask for Referrals
- ☐ Review Goals
- ☐ Refer Another Business
- ☐ Plan For Next Week

SPHERE OF INFLUENCE CALLS

1.
2.
3.
4.
5.

NOTES

WEEKLY PLANNER
Week 34
Date_____

MONDAY

TUESDAY

WEDNESDAY

THURSDAY

FRIDAY

SATURDAY

SUNDAY

TO DO

☐ Post on Social Media at least 3xs

☐ Complete Touch Point Activity

☐ Add Contacts to Database

☐ Ask for Referrals

☐ Review Goals

☐ Refer Another Business

☐ Plan For Next Week

SPHERE OF INFLUENCE CALLS

1.
2.
3.
4.
5.

NOTES

WEEKLY PLANNER
Week 35

Date_____

MONDAY

TUESDAY

WEDNESDAY

THURSDAY

FRIDAY

SATURDAY

SUNDAY

TO DO

☐ Post on Social Media at least 3xs

☐ Complete Touch Point Activity

☐ Add Contacts to Database

☐ Ask for Referrals

☐ Review Goals

☐ Refer Another Business

☐ Plan For Next Week

SPHERE OF INFLUENCE CALLS

1.

2.

3.

4.

5.

NOTES

WEEKLY PLANNER
Week 36

Date_____

MONDAY

TUESDAY

WEDNESDAY

THURSDAY

FRIDAY

SATURDAY

SUNDAY

TO DO

- [ ] Post on Social Media at least 3xs
- [ ] Complete Touch Point Activity
- [ ] Add Contacts to Database
- [ ] Ask for Referrals
- [ ] Review Goals
- [ ] Refer Another Business
- [ ] Plan For Next Week

SPHERE OF INFLUENCE CALLS

1.
2.
3.
4.
5.

NOTES

WEEKLY PLANNER
Week 37   Date_____

MONDAY

TUESDAY

WEDNESDAY

THURSDAY

FRIDAY

SATURDAY

SUNDAY

TO DO

- [ ] Post on Social Media at least 3xs
- [ ] Complete Touch Point Activity
- [ ] Add Contacts to Database
- [ ] Ask for Referrals
- [ ] Review Goals
- [ ] Refer Another Business
- [ ] Plan For Next Week

SPHERE OF INFLUENCE CALLS

1.
2.
3.
4.
5.

NOTES

WEEKLY PLANNER
Week 38

Date_____

MONDAY

TUESDAY

WEDNESDAY

THURSDAY

FRIDAY

SATURDAY

SUNDAY

TO DO

- ☐ Post on Social Media at least 3xs
- ☐ Complete Touch Point Activity
- ☐ Add Contacts to Database
- ☐ Ask for Referrals
- ☐ Review Goals
- ☐ Refer Another Business
- ☐ Plan For Next Week

SPHERE OF INFLUENCE CALLS

1.
2.
3.
4.
5.

NOTES

WEEKLY PLANNER
Week 39

Date_____

MONDAY

TUESDAY

WEDNESDAY

THURSDAY

FRIDAY

SATURDAY

SUNDAY

TO DO

- [ ] Post on Social Media at least 3xs
- [ ] Complete Touch Point Activity
- [ ] Add Contacts to Database
- [ ] Ask for Referrals
- [ ] Review Goals
- [ ] Refer Another Business
- [ ] Plan For Next Week

SPHERE OF INFLUENCE CALLS

1.
2.
3.
4.
5.

NOTES

Quarter 3 Recap

What worked well?

Which activity did you feel most comfortable performing? Why?

Which activity was the least comfortable? Why?

Was it difficult or easy asking for referrals? Why?

How many referral leads did you receive over the past quarter?

Did you meet any new service partners you can refer to your sphere?

Did your database grow?

What adjustments need to be made for the next quarter?

Quarter 4
Planner

Quarter 4 Goals

Referral Goals This Quarter
Remember to refer to your goal projections sheet   _____

# of Referrals Received Last Quarter   _____

Referral Leads Converted to Business   _____

Commission Earned from Referral Business   _____

☑ Core Activities (Consistent Activities)
☑ Post on Social Media 3xs a week

☑ Call 2-5 Contacts in Sphere of Influence a week

☑ Refer business to at least 7 other service partners during the quarter.

Your Pick (Activities of Your Choice) 4x4=16
Pick 4 other touch points to implement 4xs time during the quarter.

☑ Touch Point 1 _____

☑ Touch Point 2 _____

☑ Touch Point 3 _____

☑ Touch Point 4 _____

WEEKLY PLANNER
Week 40

Date_____

MONDAY

TUESDAY

WEDNESDAY

THURSDAY

FRIDAY

SATURDAY

SUNDAY

TO DO

- ☐ Post on Social Media at least 3xs
- ☐ Complete Touch Point Activity
- ☐ Add Contacts to Database
- ☐ Ask for Referrals
- ☐ Review Goals
- ☐ Refer Another Business
- ☐ Plan For Next Week

SPHERE OF INFLUENCE CALLS

1.
2.
3.
4.
5.

NOTES

WEEKLY PLANNER
Week 41   Date_____

MONDAY

TUESDAY

WEDNESDAY

THURSDAY

FRIDAY

SATURDAY

SUNDAY

TO DO

- [ ] Post on Social Media at least 3xs
- [ ] Complete Touch Point Activity
- [ ] Add Contacts to Database
- [ ] Ask for Referrals
- [ ] Review Goals
- [ ] Refer Another Business
- [ ] Plan For Next Week

SPHERE OF INFLUENCE CALLS

1.
2.
3.
4.
5.

NOTES

WEEKLY PLANNER
Week 42

Date_____

MONDAY

TUESDAY

WEDNESDAY

THURSDAY

FRIDAY

SATURDAY

SUNDAY

TO DO

☐ Post on Social Media at least 3xs

☐ Complete Touch Point Activity

☐ Add Contacts to Database

☐ Ask for Referrals

☐ Review Goals

☐ Refer Another Business

☐ Plan For Next Week

SPHERE OF INFLUENCE CALLS

1.

2.

3.

4.

5.

NOTES

WEEKLY PLANNER
Week 43

Date_____

MONDAY

TUESDAY

WEDNESDAY

THURSDAY

FRIDAY

SATURDAY

SUNDAY

TO DO

- [ ] Post on Social Media at least 3xs
- [ ] Complete Touch Point Activity
- [ ] Add Contacts to Database
- [ ] Ask for Referrals
- [ ] Review Goals
- [ ] Refer Another Business
- [ ] Plan For Next Week

SPHERE OF INFLUENCE CALLS

1.
2.
3.
4.
5.

NOTES

WEEKLY PLANNER
Week 44

Date_____

MONDAY

TUESDAY

WEDNESDAY

THURSDAY

FRIDAY

SATURDAY

SUNDAY

TO DO

- [ ] Post on Social Media at least 3xs
- [ ] Complete Touch Point Activity
- [ ] Add Contacts to Database
- [ ] Ask for Referrals
- [ ] Review Goals
- [ ] Refer Another Business
- [ ] Plan For Next Week

SPHERE OF INFLUENCE CALLS

1.
2.
3.
4.
5.

NOTES

WEEKLY PLANNER
Week 45   Date_____

MONDAY

TUESDAY

WEDNESDAY

THURSDAY

FRIDAY

SATURDAY

SUNDAY

TO DO

- [ ] Post on Social Media at least 3xs
- [ ] Complete Touch Point Activity
- [ ] Add Contacts to Database
- [ ] Ask for Referrals
- [ ] Review Goals
- [ ] Refer Another Business
- [ ] Plan For Next Week

SPHERE OF INFLUENCE CALLS

1.
2.
3.
4.
5.

NOTES

WEEKLY PLANNER
Week 46   Date_____

MONDAY

TUESDAY

WEDNESDAY

THURSDAY

FRIDAY

SATURDAY

SUNDAY

TO DO

- ☐ Post on Social Media at least 3xs
- ☐ Complete Touch Point Activity
- ☐ Add Contacts to Database
- ☐ Ask for Referrals
- ☐ Review Goals
- ☐ Refer Another Business
- ☐ Plan For Next Week

SPHERE OF INFLUENCE CALLS

1.
2.
3.
4.
5.

NOTES

WEEKLY PLANNER
Week 47

Date_____

MONDAY

TUESDAY

WEDNESDAY

THURSDAY

FRIDAY

SATURDAY

SUNDAY

TO DO

- [ ] Post on Social Media at least 3xs
- [ ] Complete Touch Point Activity
- [ ] Add Contacts to Database
- [ ] Ask for Referrals
- [ ] Review Goals
- [ ] Refer Another Business
- [ ] Plan For Next Week

SPHERE OF INFLUENCE CALLS

1.
2.
3.
4.
5.

NOTES

WEEKLY PLANNER
Week 48

Date_____

MONDAY

TUESDAY

WEDNESDAY

THURSDAY

FRIDAY

SATURDAY

SUNDAY

TO DO

☐ Post on Social Media at least 3xs

☐ Complete Touch Point Activity

☐ Add Contacts to Database

☐ Ask for Referrals

☐ Review Goals

☐ Refer Another Business

☐ Plan For Next Week

SPHERE OF INFLUENCE CALLS

1.

2.

3.

4.

5.

NOTES

WEEKLY PLANNER
Week 49

Date_____

MONDAY

TUESDAY

WEDNESDAY

THURSDAY

FRIDAY

SATURDAY

SUNDAY

TO DO

- [ ] Post on Social Media at least 3xs
- [ ] Complete Touch Point Activity
- [ ] Add Contacts to Database
- [ ] Ask for Referrals
- [ ] Review Goals
- [ ] Refer Another Business
- [ ] Plan For Next Week

SPHERE OF INFLUENCE CALLS

1.
2.
3.
4.
5.

NOTES

WEEKLY PLANNER
Week 50   Date_____

MONDAY

TUESDAY

WEDNESDAY

THURSDAY

FRIDAY

SATURDAY

SUNDAY

TO DO

☐ Post on Social Media at least 3xs

☐ Complete Touch Point Activity

☐ Add Contacts to Database

☐ Ask for Referrals

☐ Review Goals

☐ Refer Another Business

☐ Plan For Next Week

SPHERE OF INFLUENCE CALLS

1.

2.

3.

4.

5.

NOTES

WEEKLY PLANNER
Week 51

Date_____

MONDAY

TUESDAY

WEDNESDAY

THURSDAY

FRIDAY

SATURDAY

SUNDAY

TO DO

- [ ] Post on Social Media at least 3xs
- [ ] Complete Touch Point Activity
- [ ] Add Contacts to Database
- [ ] Ask for Referrals
- [ ] Review Goals
- [ ] Refer Another Business
- [ ] Plan For Next Week

SPHERE OF INFLUENCE CALLS

1.
2.
3.
4.
5.

NOTES

WEEKLY PLANNER
Week 52   Date_____

MONDAY

TUESDAY

WEDNESDAY

THURSDAY

FRIDAY

SATURDAY

SUNDAY

TO DO

- [ ] Post on Social Media at least 3xs
- [ ] Complete Touch Point Activity
- [ ] Add Contacts to Database
- [ ] Ask for Referrals
- [ ] Review Goals
- [ ] Refer Another Business
- [ ] Plan For Next Week

SPHERE OF INFLUENCE CALLS

1.
2.
3.
4.
5.

NOTES

Quarter 4 Recap

What worked well?

Which activity did you feel most comfortable performing? Why?

Which activity was the least comfortable? Why?

Was it difficult or easy asking for referrals? Why?

How many referral leads did you receive over the past quarter?

Did you meet any new service partners you can refer to your sphere?

Did your database grow?

What adjustments need to be made for the next quarter?

52 Week Recap

You have had 52 weeks to work the plan.
Let's see how your hard work paid off!

Business Plan Review

1. What was your financial goal at the beginning of the year?

2. What were your actual earnings?

Sphere of Influence Growth

1. How many contacts did you have at the beginning of the year?

2. How many contacts did you have after 52 weeks?

Referral Business

1. How many referrals did you receive?

2. How many referrals did you convert to sales?

3. How much of your earnings were from referrals?

Get Ready For Next Year

1. What is your financial goal for next year?

2. How many referrals are you seeking for next year?

Use the goal worksheet to plan for next year.

Pick up "Recipe for Referrals" the complete planning workbook!

CONGRATULATIONS!!
Keep building your referral based business!

Glossary of Terms

Contact Relationship Management (CRM) - Technology used to manage relationships and contact with consumers and clients.

Direct Mail Marketing - Marketing that focuses on sending physical correspondence directly to the consumer via the postal system.

Niche Market - An area of the real estate market that an agent specializes or is an expert.

Referral - Someone who uses a product or service based on the recommendation or testimony of another person they know, like or trust.

Referral Based Business - Real estate business that is based soley on referrals from past clients, service partners and people who know, like and trust you.

Referral Based Marketing - Marketing that focuses on referrals to grow business.

Sphere of Influence - A group of people who know, like and trust you. This list can include, friends, family, service partners, past clients and other real estate agents.

Service Partners - Real estate professionals that support your business. This list could include attorneys, lenders, home inspectors, insurance providers other real estate agents etc.

Touch Point - Any time someone comes in contact with you, your message, brand or marketing. This can be anytime before or after the real estate transaction is completed.

Made in the USA
Middletown, DE
18 October 2023

41047224R00055